# ANDY CAPP
## AT 50

**CELEBRATING HALF A CENTURY OF LAUGHS**

# ANDY CAPP

## AT 50

CELEBRATING HALF A CENTURY OF LAUGHS

D&C
David and Charles

Edited by Duncan Ion

Cartoons: Reg Smythe, Roger Kettle & Roger Mahoney
Graphics: Richard Sunderland

Visit Andy at www.andycapp.com

A DAVID & CHARLES BOOK
Copyright © David & Charles Limited 2006

David & Charles is an F+W Publications Inc. company
4700 East Galbraith Road
Cincinnati, OH 45236

First published in the UK in 2006

Copyright © MGN Limited 2006

A catalogue record for this book is available from the British Library.

ISBN-13: 978-0-7153-2566-7 paperback
ISBN-10: 0-7153-2566-3 paperback

Printed in China by RR Donnelley
for David & Charles
Brunel House     Newton Abbot     Devon

Commissioning Editor  Neil Baber
Assistant Editor  Louise Clark
Design Assistant  Eleanor Stafford
Production Controller  Kelly Smith

Visit our website at www.davidandcharles.co.uk

David & Charles books are available from all good bookshops;
alternatively you can contact our Orderline on 0870 9908222 or write
to us at FREEPOST EX2 110, D&C Direct, Newton Abbot, TQ12 4ZZ
(no stamp required UK only); US customers call 800-289-0963 and
Canadian customers call 800-840-5220.

# FIFTY YEARS OF ANDY CAPP

It is 50 years since Reg Smythe first introduced Andy Capp to the public in the pages of the *Daily Mirror* in 1957. This working class lad (who has never worked!) has since provided an interval of wry humour in our lives everyday – quite an achievement.

Smythe was already working as a cartoonist for the *Daily Mirror* when he came up with Andy Capp in response to the paper's desire to improve sales in the North of England. Andy reflected the supposed interests of the working class northern man of the day; football (less frequently cricket and rugby), fishing, pigeon racing, darts, snooker, betting on the horses and most of all drinking beer in the pub. He and his long-suffering wife Flo are caricatures very loosely based on a number of people that Smythe grew up with in the North Eastern town of Hartlepool in that austere period just after the Second World War.

Although the original character looks somewhat different to the modern Andy, it didn't take long for Smythe to perfect him and Andy has remained essentially unchanged since the 1960s. The biggest alterations to his physical appearance coming with the addition of colour to the strip in the 1980s, and the removal of the once ever-present cigarette, in line with modern attitudes to smoking.

The eternal struggle between the layabout husband and the long-suffering wife is as relevant today as it was in the 1950s. As a cartoon character with virtually no redeeming features, it might be surprising that Andy has survived the test of time and fashion. But perhaps it is precisely the progress of society towards scrupulous equality of the sexes, governmental 'nannying' over the evils of drinking, smoking and gambling and 'politically correct' attitudes in general that make Andy all the more potent a satirical vehicle.

From humble northern origins, Andy has spread far and wide, appearing in newspapers in more than 50 countries around the world and, beyond the printed page, spawning a stage musical and a TV series, and even his own website. The character continued after Reg Smythe's death in 1998 thanks to the stock of more than a year's worth of unpublished cartoons. When this supply was exhausted, the baton was expertly taken up by Roger Kettle and Roger Mahoney who continue to provide our regular dose of Andy to this day.

In celebration of the anniversary we have assembled a selection of classic Andy Capp cartoons from previous decades, as well as the best of this year's new cartoons. So, read the book, smile at Andy's antics, sympathize with Flo and raise a glass to fifty years of Andy Capp.

*"When THIS boy gets a cold I don't know whether to send for a doctor or a drama critic."*

*"'Ard lines, Mr. Ainsley, yer rent came in third!"*

*"I've got it going now, thank you ...
I said I've got it going ...
I said I've – do you mind?"*

*"'Course yer can 'ave a drop o' port, pet – who's treatin' yer?"*

"I'm *the party she belongs to!*"

"Remember now, I don't want to be invited back again – so just be yourself."

"Florrie! Yer shouldn't be doin' that, yer just out of 'ospital – make two journeys!"

"Play yer deuce!"

"I know we're late for the second 'alf, mate, but it can't be 'elped – there's only one bottle opener between the eleven of us."

"First time you've been lucky at the dogs for ages – what are we goin' to do wi' the money ...?"

*"Landlord! There's summat wrong with the juke box!"*

*"I kept tellin' Chalkie that I was takin' yer to the pictures, but 'e insisted on draggin' me in 'ere!"*

*"I 'ear Chalkie was in 'ere last night – was I with 'im?"*

*"I saw a good job advertised this mornin', so I went round to see abaht it straight away – yer start tomorrow."*

"I can't bear to see yer strugglin' blindly with that lot, Florrie, lemme give yer a 'and."

"Did yer 'ear me? I said I'm goin' 'ome to mother!"

"I'm not the one to let the price of a mere 'at come between us, Florrie – take it back!"

*"Don't be ridiculous!"*

*"Don't think I'm gettin' at yer, Andy,
but i'd be obliged if yer'd oil me
lawnmower now an' then."*

THUMP

I'M SERIOUSLY THINKING OF SENDING YOU OFF WHEN THE GAME STARTS!

X240

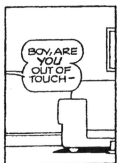

ONE OF MY PIGEONS IS LOOKING A BIT SICKLY, PET — WHILE YOU'RE OUT WOULD YOU ASK THE VET TO CALL ROUND?

BOY, ARE YOU OUT OF TOUCH—

THE ONLY PEOPLE WHO MAKE HOUSE CALLS THESE DAYS ARE BURGLARS

X262

ON SECOND THOUGHTS, PERCY, I'D PREFER TO GO AN' PLAY SQUASH

YOU'RE THE BOSS, DARLING, IF YOU PREFER SQUASH TO A GAME OF DARTS, THAT'S WHAT WE'LL DO

YEUK!

PERCY, PERCY—

THERE'S NO TWIT LIKE AN OLD TWIT WHO GOES OUT WITH A YOUNG TWIT!

N226

# ANDY CAPP
## AT 50

I THINK AGE HAS FINALLY CAUGHT UP WITH ME THIS SEASON, PET

OH, DON'T BE SILLY

I DID WELL NOT TO ADD "THAT HAPPENED YEARS AGO"

FANCY GOING TO THE SEASIDE THIS WEEKEND, PET? WE HAVEN'T BEEN FOR AGES

WELL THERE'S A COINCIDENCE

I READ IN THE PAPER THE LADIES' BEACH VOLLEYBALL FINALS ARE ON THIS WEEKEND

REALLY? I HADN'T NOTICED

ISN'T IT FUNNY HOW A BEER ALWAYS TASTES BETTER AFTER A HARD DAY'S WORK?

I'D GO WITH A "NO COMMENT" FOR THAT ONE, PET

I'M EXHAUSTED — THE BATHROOM DRAIN GOT BLOCKED

I HAD TO GO AND GET THIS LONG, THIN STICK

HONESTLY, I WAS BANGING IT ON THE FLOOR FOR AGES BEFORE FLO CAME UP AND FIXED IT!

ISN'T THAT THE GUY WHO BEAT YOU IN THE POOL FINAL?

YEAH, THAT'S HIM IN HIS FLASH CAR — IT'S GOT A DEVICE THAT PREVENTS PEOPLE LETTING DOWN THE TYRES

UM...SO I'VE HEARD

I SEE THAT NEW INDONESIAN RESTAURANT HAS OPENED

LET'S SEE — WE'VE NOW GOT INDIAN, CHINESE, FRENCH, ITALIAN AND INDONESIAN

YOU'RE SPOILT FOR CHOICE FOR PLACES NOT TO TAKE ME

WHAT'S UP?

I'VE GOT A REALLY SORE NECK

FLO ASKED ME TO PAINT THE KITCHEN CEILING TODAY,...

...AND I THINK I DAMAGED IT SHAKING MY HEAD

WE HAD A SIMPLY *FABULOUS* MEAL IN THE GRAND HOTEL LAST NIGHT!

AH, YES, THE GRAND HOTEL— I'VE BEEN THERE MANY TIMES

WAS THAT WHEN YOU HAD THE CLEANING JOB THERE?

SHH

I SAW ANDY THIS AFTERNOON— HE WAS LOOKING PRETTY DOWN

HE GETS A BIT DEPRESSED IN THE SUMMER WHEN THERE'S NO FOOTBALL ON T.V.

SWEARING AT TENNIS ISN'T AS SATISFYING

WHY ARE YOU SO LATE?

IT'S ALL YOUR MOTHER'S FAULT

MUM WAS IN THE PUB?

NO — THAT'S THE POINT. IF SHE *HAD* BEEN, I'D HAVE COME HOME EARLY

I BEAT MY RECORD LAST NIGHT

WHAT RECORD?

IT TOOK ME AGES BUT I THREW A POTATO CRISP EIGHT FEET

YOU'RE A VERY SAD MAN, CHALKIE

I HOPE TO REACH TEN

IT'S BEEN SOME WEEK, ANDY — FIRST, THE WIFE LEAVES ME AND THEN MY DOG DIES

THAT'S LIFE FOR YOU, WALTER

JUST WHEN YOU'RE ON A HIGH, SOMETHING COMES ALONG TO KNOCK YOU DOWN

HOW'S FLO?

I WON'T LIE TO YOU, RUBE — SHE'S NOT GOOD

SHE'S TAKEN A COUPLE OF PILLS AND GONE TO BED

SO THIS SHOP ASSISTANT THOUGHT FLO AND HER MUM WERE SISTERS?

SH! YOU'LL GET HER GOING AGAIN!

I FELL OUT OF BED AT TEN O'CLOCK THIS MORNING...

... I THEN WATCHED T.V. FOR THREE HOURS THEN SLEPT ALL AFTERNOON ON THE COUCH

I THINK I'VE JUST HAD THE PERFECT DAY!

HOW'S ANDY, FLO? I HEAR HE'S HURT HIS BACK

HE'S FINE, VICAR — IT WAS JUST ONE OF THOSE THINGS THAT COULD HAPPEN TO ANYONE

HE WAS BALANCING ON A STACK OF PAINT TINS, TRYING TO REACH THE PURSE I'D HIDDEN ON TOP OF THE WARDROBE WHEN HIS FOOT SLIPPED

I'M STARTING TO THINK *ALL* MEN ARE USELESS, AUNTIE FLO

IT'S SAD TO HEAR YOU TALK LIKE THAT, MAUREEN

I'D HOPED THAT, BY NOW, YOU'D *KNOW* THEY WERE ALL USELESS

I THINK THAT'S ANDY'S STRONGEST ASSET IN THE GAME — HIS WONDERFUL BALANCE

MOST PLAYERS WOULD HAVE FALLEN OVER AFTER SWINGING A PUNCH LIKE THAT

YOUNG DEBBIE AT WORK IS THINKING ABOUT GETTING A TATTOO

SHE WANTS TO GET A LITTLE CHERUB TATTOOED ON HER STOMACH — I'M TRYING TO TALK HER OUT OF IT

TELL HER WHEN SHE'S SIXTY IT'LL LOOK LIKE A BULLDOG

THEY'VE BEEN TALKING AT WORK ABOUT THIS NEW CRAZE FOR "POWER WALKING"

IT'S NOT NEW— ANDY'S BEEN DOING IT FOR AGES

EXCEPT HE CALLS IT "OPENING TIME"

I'LL JUST GO AND PUT THE SHOPPING AWAY

EEK!

OH, SORRY, PET— I FORGOT TO TELL YOU I'D PUT SOME MAGGOTS IN THE FRIDGE FOR FISHING

IT'S NOT THAT— I JUST NOTICED YOU'VE WASHED YOUR COFFEE MUG

THAT TAKES ME BACK, PET

REMEMBER OUR CYCLING TRIP? AH, YES— YOUR IDEA OF A ROMANTIC FIRST ANNIVERSARY

YOU GAVE ME A PUNCTURE REPAIR KIT FOR A PRESENT

I'LL JUST CHECK YOUR EMPLOYMENT DETAILS

BANK LOANS

HMM. IT SAYS HERE YOU'VE NEVER WORKED IN YOUR WHOLE LIFE

BANK LOA

I PREFER TO SAY I'VE NEVER BEEN FIRED IN MY WHOLE LIFE

BAN LOA

SOMETIMES, YOU'D NEVER GUESS HE'S BEEN PLAYING ALL THESE YEARS

HE'S STILL GOT HIS ENTHUSIASM, HIS AGGRESSION, A BIT OF PACE ...

... AND THEN HE DOES HIS "CHARLESTON" GOAL CELEBRATION

WELCOME TO THE TWILIGHT ZONE

THAT WEIRD PERIOD OF TIME BETWEEN HIM GETTING OUT OF BED AND MAKING HIS WAY TO THE COUCH

THERE'S AN IDEA FOR CHALKIE'S CHRISTMAS

A NEW TOOL KIT— HE'S HAD HIS OLD ONE FOR OVER TWENTY YEARS

JUST LIKE ANDY

ALTHOUGH I'M ASSUMING CHALKIE'S ACTUALLY OPENED HIS

SO HOW ARE THINGS AFTER UNIVERSITY, SALLY?

GREAT— I'M TAKING A GAP YEAR BEFORE STARTING WORK

ANDY DID THAT

ALTHOUGH HIS WAS MORE OF A GAP LIFE

I HAVEN'T SEEN YOUR MOTHER-IN-LAW IN HERE FOR A WHILE

SHE'S A BIT UNDER THE WEATHER

NOTHING SERIOUS?

STRESS FRACTURES OF THE EYEBROWS FROM SCOWLING

THAT GUTTERING REALLY NEEDS FIXING

TROUBLE IS, THE LADDER I'VE GOT IS ONLY ABOUT EIGHT FEET

I DON'T THINK FLO'S GOING TO BE ABLE TO REACH IT

HI, FLO — HOW'S ANDY? I HAVEN'T SEEN HIM IN AGES

YOU'RE OBVIOUSLY LOOKING IN THE WRONG PLACES, BERT

HAVE YOU TRIED OUR COUCH?

I'M HAVING A "SPEED DATING" NIGHT IN HERE NEXT WEEK

YOU KNOW — YOU GET THREE MINUTES TO FIND OUT IF YOU'RE COMPATIBLE WITH A WOMAN

THAT'S NOT LONG

I MEAN, BY THE TIME SHE GOES AND BUYS YOU A DRINK ....

I'VE JUST BEEN TALKING TO RUBY!

WHEN *SHE* GETS HOME FROM WORK, CHALKIE HAS A MEAL READY FOR HER — ANY THOUGHTS?

WELL, I'LL ASK HIM PET, BUT I DOUBT IF HE'LL COOK FOR YOU AS WELL

...SO HE HITS THIS 7-IRON TO ABOUT FOUR FEET FROM THE PIN

REMEMBER, I'M IN THE GREENSIDE BUNKER SO I TAKE OUT MY SAND IRON

YOU'LL NEVER GUESS WHAT HAPPENS NEXT

I THINK I CAN

MAN IN PUB PUNCHES BORING GOLFER

ARE YOU COMING TO WATCH THE MATCH, FLO?

NOT TODAY, PET— I'M A BIT BUSY

YOU CAN TELL ME HOW YOU GOT SENT OFF WHEN YOU COME HOME

TCH! TCH!

STAGGERING ABOUT THE STREETS AT THIS TIME OF NIGHT — WHAT'S FLO GOING TO SAY?

SHE'LL BE UPSET, VICAR, BUT I'M SURE SHE'LL FORGIVE YOU

SO, LADIES — WHEN WAS THE LAST TIME YOUR MAN BOUGHT YOU FLOWERS?

LET ME THINK — IT WAS YESTERDAY...

...THAT I ASKED MYSELF THE SAME QUESTION AND THE ANSWER IS THIRTY YEARS AGO

RUBY WANTS TO GO ON ONE OF THOSE WHALE-WATCHING TRIPS

I FIND THAT REALLY CREEPY

I MEAN, WHAT'S NEXT — DOLPHIN-OGLING?

SOMETIMES YOU SCARE ME, CHALKIE

YOU PROMISED YOU'D COME WITH ME TO MY MOTHER'S TONIGHT!

WHAT'S MORE IMPORTANT TO YOU? PLAYING POOL IN THE PUB...

...AND IT WOULD HAVE BEEN NICE IF YOU'D WAITED FOR THE OPTION

MAY I SAY HOW MOVED I WAS BY YOUR SERMON ABOUT THE GOOD SAMARITAN?

YOU KNOW, HOW HE HELPED PEOPLE IN NEED

HOW MUCH DO YOU WANT TO BORROW?

TCH! THAT IS SO INSULTING THAT I'LL FORCE MYSELF TO ACCEPT A TENNER

IT'S BEEN GREAT SEEING YOU AGAIN AFTER ALL THESE YEARS, FLO

WHY DON'T YOU AND ANDY COME ROUND TO OUR PLACE FOR A MEAL ON SATURDAY?

LOVE TO!

THOSE ARE THE ONLY INVITATIONS WE GET THESE DAYS — FROM PEOPLE WHO'VE FORGOTTEN WHAT ANDY'S LIKE

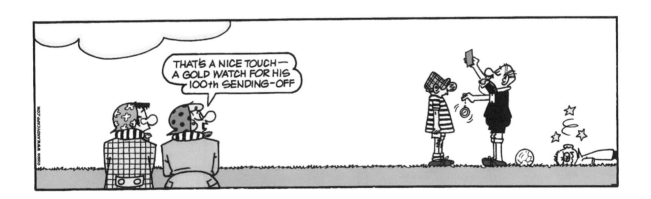

WHAT *IS* THIS?

IT'S A RECIPE I SAW IN A MAGAZINE

"HOW TO POISON YOUR HUSBAND MONTHLY?"

WHETHER IT TAKES DAYS, MONTHS, OR EVEN YEARS, I WANT YOU TO KNOW THAT I'LL WAIT FOR YOU

BEAUTY SALON

VERY FUNNY

THERE'S YOUR MUM-IN-LAW ACROSS THE STREET

SO IT IS

LOOKS LIKE SHE'S STRUGGLING TO CARRY THOSE SHOPPING BAGS

TCH! I'D BETTER DO SOMETHING

I'LL WALK ON THE INSIDE IN CASE SHE SPOTS ME

THE WORST WEDDING I'VE EVER BEEN TO — THE GROOM DID A RUNNER BEFORE IT STARTED

THE BEST WEDDING I'VE EVER BEEN TO — THE GROOM DID A RUNNER BEFORE IT STARTED!

SO WHAT DOES IT TASTE LIKE?

I'M NOT SURE

I DON'T THINK IT TASTES OF ANYTHING MUCH

THAT'S WHAT I THOUGHT

THEY'RE DISCUSSING WATER

I BUMPED INTO CHARLIE BRYSON IN TOWN

HE SAID I WAS LOOKING GORGEOUS!

SO HOW IS MAD CHARLIE?

GOSH, THERE'S A SURPRISE...

...USUALLY WHEN I GET HOME HE'S GOT A TUXEDO ON AND A ROSE BETWEEN HIS TEETH

THERE'S FLO'S MUM, CROSSING THE STREET

A DRIVER IS TOOTING HIS HORN AND SWEARING AT HER

BIG MISTAKE, MISTER

NOW SHE'S CROSSING THE STREET, CARRYING TWO WING MIRRORS AND A WINDSCREEN WIPER

I CAN GET FLO A HUGE BUNCH OF FLOWERS AND STILL HAVE ENOUGH FOR A BEER!

BETTING OFFICE

OR A LARGE BUNCH AND A COUPLE OF BEERS

OR MAYBE A SMALL BUNCH AND A FEW BEERS

HIC

IF THERE WAS A FILM OF YOUR LIFE, WHICH ACTOR WOULD PLAY YOU?

BRAD PITT— WHAT ABOUT YOU?

MEL GIBSON

YES, I CAN SEE THAT

THE SCARY THING IS THAT THEY'RE SERIOUS

ELSIE SMITH'S INVITED US TO AFTERNOON TEA ON THE TWENTY-NINTH

I CAN'T MAKE IT ON THAT DATE

WHY— WHAT ARE YOU DOING?

ANYTHING

ISN'T IT FUNNY HOW FOOTBALLERS HAVE SPLIT PERSONALITIES?

TAKE ANDY FOR INSTANCE — ON THE FIELD HE'S LOUD-MOUTHED AND OBNOXIOUS...,

...AND YET, OFF THE FIELD, HE'S — WELL MAYBE THAT'S NOT A GOOD EXAMPLE

TCH! ANOTHER LOSER!

ME TOO

OH, WAIT—I WON! THAT WAS NUMBER TWO— THE PRETTY ONE WITH THE CUTE BLINKERS AND THE FUNNY NOSE BAND!

ANDY? ANDY?

I HEAR YOUR MOTHER-IN-LAW'S GOING ON A CRUISE

YES—SHE LIKES A BIT OF A CHANGE EVERY SO OFTEN

GIVES HER A CHANCE TO BE ANNOYING ON WATER INSTEAD OF LAND

A NAP IN THE MORNING, A NAP IN THE AFTERNOON AND A NAP IN THE EVENING

HE'S A HUNDRED AND TWENTY WINKS A DAY MAN

CINEMA

WELL, THAT WAS PRETTY DISAPPOINTING

THE SCRIPT WAS WEAK, THE DIRECTION WAS POOR...

...AND GEORGE CLOONEY ONLY TOOK HIS SHIRT OFF TWICE

SHAMEFUL

THAT'S MY FAVOURITE WAY OF KEEPING FIT

LAUGHING AT JOGGERS ALWAYS GETS THE OLD HEART PUMPING

BEFORE I APPROVE YOUR LOAN, MISTER CAPP, I'LL JUST CHECK YOUR DETAILS ON THE COMPUTER

BANK LOANS

BANK LOANS

I'VE NEVER SEEN THE FLASHING TRIPLE RED ALERT BEFORE

BRIGHT, ISN'T IT?

BANK LOANS

...SO I PUT MY FOOT DOWN — I TOLD HIM IT WAS TIME HE TOOK HIS OPPORTUNITIES...

...I TOLD HIM THE WORLD WAS HIS OYSTER

WHAT DID HE SAY?

HE'S ALLERGIC TO SEAFOOD

CATCH ANYTHING, ANDY?

NAH,...

...BUT THAT'S NOT IMPORTANT — THE JOY OF FISHING IS JUST GETTING AWAY FROM IT ALL

WELL LIED

THANK YOU

HI, RUBE — FLO'S ROUND AT HER MOTHER'S SO I'M MAKING MYSELF SOMETHING TO EAT

YOU KNOW WHEN YOU HEAT BEANS IN A PAN?

YES

WHAT'S THE BEST WAY TO PUT THE FLAMES OUT?

WHAT WOULD YOU DO IF YOU WON THE LOTTERY?

FIRST, I'D GO AND SEE RUBY'S PARENTS — THEY'VE NEVER HAD MUCH MONEY

SO YOU'D GO GLOATING?

YES, I WOULD

I'M STARVING, AND FLO WON'T BE BACK FROM WORK FOR AGES

TCH! FOR GOODNESS' SAKE, LISTEN TO YOURSELF — ARE YOU HELPLESS?

JUST GET UP, PHONE HER AND TELL HER TO COME HOME EARLY

FORE!

I THINK HONESTY IN A MAN IS SO IMPORTANT

I AGREE

ON MY TWENTY FIRST BIRTHDAY, I VOWED ALWAYS TO TELL THE TRUTH

AND NOW, TWO YEARS ON, I STILL STAND BY THAT

TCH! JUST LOOK AT YOU

YOU'RE FLAT BROKE, YET YOU'RE LYING ON THE COUCH DOING NOTHING

YOU SHOULD BE OUT ON ON THE STREET, LOOKING FOR SOMEWHERE TO DO THE LOTTERY

PHEW! WHAT A DAY!

WHAT YOU NEED IS SOME BOC'N'BOW AT MY PLACE

SOME WHAT?

BOX OF CHOCOLATES, BOTTLE OF WINE

GIMME TWO MINUTES!

YOU'VE GOT TO ADMIRE ANDY— HIS STAMINA IS AMAZING

HE CAN STILL SWEAR TWICE AS LOUD AS PLAYERS HALF HIS AGE

ANDY— TRACK BACK WITH THEIR WINGER WHEN HE BREAKS FROM DEFENSE!

STAY GOALSIDE OF HIM SO YOU CAN INTERCEPT ANY THROUGH BALL!

OW!

OR POKE HIM IN THE EYE

I HEAR FLO'S GOT LARYNGITIS — HOW IS SHE?

SHE'S GOT A DISLOCATED SHOULDER AS WELL

HOW ON EARTH DID SHE DO THAT?

TRYING TO NAG ME IN SEMAPHORE

WHAT IF I *HAD* WORKED REALLY HARD AND BECOME A HUGE SUCCESS?

FLO WOULD HAVE HATED THE TRAPPINGS THAT GO WITH THAT KIND OF GLITZY LIFESTYLE

I AM *SO* THOUGHTFUL

SHE LEFT ME, ANDY— THE NIGHT BEFORE OUR TWENTIETH WEDDING ANNIVERSARY

I WAS ACTUALLY WRAPPING HER PRESENT WHEN SHE WALKED OUT

HAVE YOU GOT THE RECEIPT?

HEH! HEH! HEH!

HEH! HEH! HEH!

LOOK—FIRSTLY, IT WASN'T FUNNY, AND SECONDLY, IT'S BEEN OVER AN HOUR NOW SINCE MY MOTHER FELL OFF HER CHAIR!

HEH! HEH! HEH!

FLO WILL BE HOME IN AN HOUR

I PROMISED HER I'D MAKE DINNER TONIGHT, SO IT'S TIME I GOT GOING

I'LL TAKE THE FUSE OUT AND PRETEND THERE'S BEEN A POWER-CUT

I HEARD YOU HAD A BIG WIN ON THE HORSES TODAY

HOW DID YOU KNOW?

I DIDN'T— UNTIL NOW

SNEAKY

THANK YOU— I HAVE A GOOD COACH

DIDN'T YOU TELL RUBY YOU'D BE HOME AT TEN?

SO? I WEAR THE TROUSERS IN MY HOUSE

YES, BUT YOU WASH THEM AND IRON THEM, TOO

OH, NO — JUST LOOK AT THIS PHONE BILL

IT'S ALL THAT RUBY'S FAULT!

SHE DOES NOTHING BUT LISTEN, LISTEN, LISTEN!

WHAT'S SO SPECIAL ABOUT THAT PIZZA?

WHAT PIZZA?

THE ONE THEY'VE GOT NAILED TO THE WALL

THAT'S THE DARTBOARD

YOU'VE GOT A LETTER FROM A TV COMPANY!

I'D FORGOTTEN ABOUT THAT!

I SENT THEM AN IDEA FOR A REALITY SHOW — WHAT DOES IT SAY?

"DEAR SIR, REGRETFULLY, WE FEEL THAT "GIANT CATAPULTS AND MOTHERS-IN-LAW"...

AH, WELL

Printed in Great Britain
by Amazon